AN INTRODUCTION TO
The Child's Conception of Geometry

G. E. T. Holloway

Principal Lecturer in Education
Sidney Webb College of Education

LONDON
ROUTLEDGE AND KEGAN PAUL

First published 1967
by Routledge & Kegan Paul Ltd
Broadway House, 68–74 Carter Lane
London, E.C.4
and National Froebel Foundation
2 Manchester Square, London, W.1

Printed in Great Britain
by Western Printing Services Ltd
Bristol

AN INTRODUCTION TO
The Child's Conception of Geometry

6/-

FURTHER ASPECTS OF PIAGET'S WORK*

1. AN INTRODUCTION TO
   The Child's Conception of Geometry

2. AN INTRODUCTION TO
   The Child's Conception of Space

* See 'Some Aspects of Piaget's Work', National Froebel
Foundation pamphlet concerned with *The Child's Conception of Number*

but which for children are the main stumbling blocks to geometrical understanding.

The majority of teachers are now familiar with the problems which children face in developing the concept of number. That children have to discover the principles of conservation, seriation, permanence of correspondence, reversibility etc., has been revealed to many of us by Piaget in his book *The Child's Conception of Number* and a great deal of related literature. We now look at children in a new light and it is our hope that these handbooks will serve to illuminate a little more of the area of the development of mathematical understanding in children.

Our aim in helping children to learn mathematics must surely be to stimulate the growth process of mathematical ideas. In order to achieve this we need to know and understand the stages of growth of such ideas and to provide experiences appropriate to each of these stages as well as to offer helpful natural bridges towards the next one. In order to enable a baby to learn to walk we first let it lie on its back and kick its legs in the air, an activity bearing very little resemblance to the ultimate attainment. This is an extreme case, but we could usefully remind ourselves of it from time to time in connection with much of Piaget's work. In providing mathematical education for our children we hope that they will eventually develop the ability to use a series of codes in order to compare, reason and predict. The practical activity involving material objects in concrete situations which Piaget's findings indicate as necessary for such a long period of time appears, at first sight, to bear about the same relation to the more developed forms of mathematical thinking as does kicking the legs in the air to walking along the ground. More and more teachers are coming to see that both of these preliminary activities are equally important, and just as any attempt to encourage a baby to walk before it has reached the necessary stage of development is doomed to failure, so also any system of mathematical information imparted to children without their having had adequate experience of the right kind actually impoverishes their development, though it may at first give it a spurious maturity.

Children must assimilate more and more experience in order to be able to make valid generalizations later. How very much later it is not easy for us to appreciate. Piaget helps us to see how long a process is the development of mathematical ideas and how very much it depends on the opportunity to manipulate material. But of course if they have the benefit of ample experiences which will help them on towards the right generalizations and mathematical ideas, they may be able to develop much more happily as well as more rapidly than Piaget's Genevese children who, like many of ours, are taught 'sums' and ununderstood ways of getting 'correct' results, instead of understanding.

We know that we think because we speak. It is not so often remembered that we speak because we can use our hands. We are increasingly accustomed to the idea of encouraging children to speak in school, and long past the state of affairs described by an infant on his return from school, who said 'I can't read and I can't write and she won't let me talk'. But perhaps we need more fully to realize the continuing value throughout the primary school of manipulative experience and practical problem-solving arising naturally from situations in which children's interest has become actively engaged.

In his introduction to *The Growth of Understanding in the Young Child* Nathan Isaacs quotes my initial response to Piaget's book *The Child's Conception of Number*, which was to describe it as being at first incomprehensible and later incredible. It is because of my feeling that the reaction of many teachers to Piaget's work is similar that I have responded to Mr. Isaacs's encouragement to embark on this present venture in the hope that it may lead many teachers to look more closely at Piaget's books and to find in them much that will influence their observation of and approach to children.

I have not attempted to do more than present a brief simplified account of the contents of Piaget's books, much of the account being in the form of direct quotation. Inevitably a great deal has been omitted and in particular almost all of the intensely interesting living material of children's own responses, and the concrete discussions to which these led. This introduction is meant to do no more than 'break the ice' by providing a broad map of Piaget's own main lines of approach and of the ground he thus covers. If this results in a more widespread study of the original its purpose will have been achieved.

I am greatly indebted to Mr. Isaacs,* who is entirely responsible for obtaining permission for this work to be undertaken and who has greatly assisted me in planning the presentation as well as having given invaluable help with the selection of the material. I am also very much indebted to Messrs. Routledge & Kegan Paul, London, and to Basic Books, New York, for giving their permission.

* It is with much regret that I record the death of Nathan Isaacs between the time of my writing this and its publication.

Table of Contents of
The Child's Conception of Geometry
(Page numbers of the original are shown in italics)

* This section is dealt with at rather greater length in *A Teachers' Guide to Reading Piaget* by M. Brearley and E. Hitchfield (Routledge & Kegan Paul, 1966).

ix

PART ONE

Introduction

I

Change of position

In order to come to an understanding of space relations a child must see himself as but one moving object among others situated in a framework of fixed references. That young children do not see themselves in this way and the sequence of development they go through before doing so is illustrated by Piaget in an experiment which involves children in a problem situation related to their own home and school environment.

By studying the way children between the ages of 4 and 10 describe a familiar walk, such as the road from home to school, or that from school to various well-known places round about, we can see clearly how they learn to describe changes of position by using landmarks and eventually link these reference points in a comprehensive system. Thus the main buildings and squares, bridges, rivers or streams (in Geneva, the Rhone and the Arve), their own school and their homes are the landmarks which go together to form a reference system, and this in turn enters into their description of changes of position.

Each child was first taken to the window of the experimental room in the school and asked to point out various landmarks. He was then faced with a tray of smooth wet sand and a collection of models of the school and near-by buildings and landmarks such as recreation grounds, bridges, etc., and asked to place them correctly on the sand tray. This was followed by the request to draw a plan of the journey home or to some local landmark and finally the model of the school was rotated through 180° and the child asked to re-arrange the other models as he thought necessary to make the plan correct.

The children's responses are grouped in stages—the experiment was unsuitable for children under 4, but from their spontaneous comments during walks it may be seen that they do have some sense of direction but are likely to be completely confused by being turned round through 180° and are unable to relate their new position to well-known landmarks as these are not necessarily stationary for them.

Even at stage 2 (4–7 years) children still think mainly in terms of their own actions, and it is not until substage 3a that they are able to achieve true representation and to divorce this at least temporarily from action. At stage 2 they can make journeys such as from school to home, but they can explain each portion of the journey only as they come to it.

In their models the positions and distances are systematically distorted by their own subjective interest or viewpoint. Thus a child may put his own (infant) school and his home close together, but place the main part of the school a long way away simply because it does not concern him. Or he may put all the bridges side by side merely because they belong to the same class of things.

Substage 3a shows the beginning of co-ordinated landmarks but not a whole co-ordinated system. This is shown by the correct grouping of parts of the plan but lack of relation between the parts—their plans show a confusion of viewpoints—each separate view being correct but the various views incorrectly related. Experimental rotation of the building results in partial success—the need for rotation of the

4

whole plan is realized, but the children fail to carry it through as they are confused by the conflict between their own position and the hypothetical one, or they forget to rotate both from back to front and from left to right. This sub-group includes children aged from 7 to nearly 10.

At substage 3b (which may sometimes begin soon after 8 years) children are able to arrange all the local landmarks in correct relation one to another (although the distances are not always in strictly correct proportion) and can solve the problem of rotation completely. This success is achieved by either of two methods. Some children group the elements in terms of sites, e.g. 'A' is here, 'B' is there, therefore 'C' must be here; others select starting points and reconstruct routes radiating from them.

II
Spontaneous measurement

The development of ideas of measurement involves both appreciation of the conservation of length and the ability to group changes of position and relate them to a co-ordinated spatial framework. Otherwise the significance of applying a succession of units along a vertical line cannot be realized, and one cannot appreciate that there must be conservation of length when a unit-object is moved.

For these reasons the present chapter is devoted to the study of spontaneous efforts at measurement. When the process has been perfected, it carries within it a great deal that is implicit. It is therefore important to investigate mensural behaviour when still in a formative state, for only thus can we hope to assess precisely the operations which enter into the psychological construction of measurement.

By way of a first series of experiments, children were shown a tower made of 12 blocks, cubes and parallelipipeds, 80 cm. in height and standing on a table. They are then asked to build a tower the same height on another table two metres away and 90 cm. lower. In order to rule out any simple reproduction of the model, the building blocks given to the children are smaller, though there are enough for a tower of the same height. A screen was, moreover, placed between the two tables, though the children were free to 'go and see' the first tower whenever they wished. Strips of paper and sticks were provided, but they were not prompted to use these until their spontaneous efforts were exhausted.

The first stage (1a and 1b) responses, typical of children aged about 4;6, involve visual comparison only. Nothing is moved except the line of vision. A typical response to the question 'Is your tower just as high as mine?' is 'Oh yes, you've only got to look.', although of course there is no exact correspondence in height—the towers are merely both tall, or huge etc. At substage 1b the model is built more nearly to the correct height, but comparison is still purely visual and no need is felt for any means of checking the estimate 'You only have to look'.

During stage 2, which lasts from 4;6 or 5 until about 7, objects are moved in the process of measurement, i.e. there is change of position. Sometimes the object in question is one of the items being compared, and sometimes it is a third term, presaging the appearance of a common measure, but there is as yet no operational transitivity. At substage 2a the visual transfer characteristic of stage 1 is supplemented by what we will term manual transfer, by which we mean that the objects to be compared are brought closer together, so that although the comparison is still visual, it is no longer comparison at a distance, but an appraisal of a whole made up of neighbouring objects. Substage 2b is marked by an interesting development which brings out yet more clearly the waning supremacy of perception taken in isolation. Children now use an intermediary term, but this is still not an independent common measuring rule, for, instead of using a third article with which to satisfy themselves that the copy is equal to the model, these children use their own bodies: at times it is the span of their

7

hands or that of their arms, while at others they avail themselves of unlikely seeming bodily reference objects (shoulders, etc.), using these to transfer a distance from one object to another. Obviously such methods are a carry-over from manual transfer (2a), just as the latter is a carry-over from visual transfer (1a and 1b). Earlier the subject moved the article itself, now he transfers a grasping or enfolding gesture, involving his hand or his arms, because he hopes that such a gesture will be a measure of the length of an object after he has let it go. This mode of behaviour, characteristic of substage 2a, we will call body transfer or object imitation. Imitation is the source of symbols and even of images. The use of a common measure can therefore be seen to have its origin in visual and manual transfer inasmuch as its initial components, both perceptual and motor, give rise to representational images which confer a symbolic value, first, on the subject's own body, and later, on any neutral object, so that these come to stand for the original transfer.

The distinguishing characteristic of stage 3 is the insight into the logical principle: $A = B$; $B = C$ therefore $A = C$. This depends on the appreciation of the conservation of length in spite of changes of position, but it is only one aspect of measurement, the other being subdivision, and only when this also is mastered can one part be given a unit value and so repeated as often as necessary. Now this gradual fusing of subdivision and change in the position of a common measuring rule occurs during stage 3, and it occurs in two substages. At stage 3a (on an average around 7 years) children use a middle term larger than the original, marking off the required length, but are unable to use a shorter one because 'It's too small', 'No, I'd need a lot of them', 'It won't work, my hand keeps moving', etc. At substage 3b, from about 8 years old onwards, the middle term may be either longer or shorter than the tower, e.g. 'Can you use this little brick?'—(He moves it stepwise up the tower, marking each position with his thumb). '*It goes 13*

8

times. (He does the same against the second tower): *It's the same.*'

The acquisition of measurement is thus a synthesis of sub-division and change of position. It is achieved through the displacements of an iterable unit which serves as middle term.

PART TWO

Conservation and
measurement of length

III
Reconstructing relations of distance

Before analysing the conservation and measurement of length
we need to study how children judge distances and how they
achieve their conservation. It may be that common usage
makes no sharp distinction between the concept of distance
and that of length. But psychologically they point to two quite
different situations which become interdependent only as a
result of a gradual development. We must therefore study them
separately. On the one hand, there is the question of the linear
size of objects like sticks or the paths along which we walk.
We shall use the term 'length' to denote this kind of size. The
term 'length' will therefore refer to the size of filled space, i.e.
to objects as such. 'Distance' will be used to refer to the linear
separation of objects, i.e. to empty space.

Because the concept of distance denotes intervals or empty
space, it is one whose study should prove rewarding not only
for problems of measurement but for examining how children
reconstruct euclidean space as a whole. Where this concept is
present, children will view space as a common medium con-
taining objects and spatial relations between objects. Such
relations will evolve to a point where co-ordinate systems are

achieved and a metrical system becomes possible. Where the concept of distance is absent, space as a medium common to several objects will be unco-ordinated. There may still be ideas of spatial relations within separate objects or isolated shapes, but there can be no understanding of measurement. The notion of distance is therefore crucial to the emergence of relations which are essential both to the development of measuring and to the elaboration of co-ordinate systems.

How then do children judge distances and come to an understanding of their conservation? In order to find an answer to these questions two lead figures, or two trees, of the same height, are set out in front of the child about 50 cm. apart. Each child is then asked if the two are 'near one another' or 'far apart'. When he has replied, a small screen, a little higher than the figures, with an adjustable opening in it, is placed between the two figures and he is asked whether the figures are still as 'near' or 'far apart' as before. The question is repeated with the opening in the screen first closed and then open. The screen is then replaced by a cube, higher than the figures and later the cube is removed and a line of bricks laid to join the two figures. In each case the same questions are asked as to whether the figures are still as 'near' or 'far apart' as they were.

The child is also asked if it is as far or near from here to there (A to B) as from there to here (B to A)—the questioner's finger being moved in the appropriate direction along the distance between the two figures in each case.

The same questions are asked after substituting a third figure for one of the first two, this being twice as high as the first and finally after one of the figures has been raised 50 cm. above the table. The children's responses again fall into three stages, the third being reached at about the age of seven.

During stage 1, which lasts up to about 4 or 5 years, the two intervals separated by the screen cannot be brought together

14

and when asked if the distance is the same, stage-1 children always say that it is less as they consider only the distance from the figure to the screen. When the figures are on different levels these children cease to consider the distance between the figures and reply in relation to the distance of each figure from themselves. When a complete line of bricks is laid between the two figures this is thought to bring them closer together.

In reply to the questions on reversibility, i.e. does AB = BA, first-stage children fail to understand the question when the figures are on the same level, but when one is higher the upward journey is judged longer than the downward one if AB and BA are considered at all; more usually the reply relates to the distance between the child and each figure.

Stage 1 Absence of overall distance. Tho (4;2). The screen (S) is placed in position between the two figures: '*They're nearer.*— Why?—(No reply) Look at them carefully. Are they nearer than before or the same?—*Nearer* (pointing to the distance AS).—And like this (screen removed)?—*Further.*'

'And is it the same from here to here (A to B) as it is from here to here (B to A, without screen and at the same level) or nearer or further?—*This way is further.* (AB).—Why?—*It's far.*—What about from here to here (BA), is it just as far?' (No reply). It is obvious that he fails to understand the question and thinks only of their respective distances from himself.

'And now, like this (B 50 cm. above A), is it as far from here to here (AB) as it is from here to here (BA) or not?—*This way is further* (indicating B).—Why?—*Because the other is higher.*' He is judging from his own point of view.

'What about these? (short A, tall C)?—*This way it's further.* (AC).—Why?—*Because he's big and the other one is little.*'

At the *second stage* (5–7 years) the subject recognizes an overall distance between A and B whatever the intervening objects. But it is significant that during substage 2a the overall distance is thought to be less when the screen is introduced because the space taken up by the screen itself must be subtracted. The width of the screen cannot be part of the distance separating A and B because it is now filled space and not empty! When the figures are at different levels, the subject responds in a way which shows that his conception of space is still not symmetrical at substage 2a: it is bound up with the effort involved in crossing it.

Ano (5;3). Two figures; no screen: '*They're near together.*—(screen:) Are they as near as they were?—*They're nearer.*—(Window in screen open:) And like this?—*They're further, because there's a hole in it.*—Why are they further?—*Because before this thing* (window) *was shut.*—(Experiment repeated.)—*It's nearer when you shut the door.*—And with this (cigarette box)?—*It's nearer because it's thicker.*(!)'

Some children at substage 2b regard distance as being different from length, distance referring to empty space and length to solid objects, hence the distance between the two figures is considered to be changed when an object is placed between them, e.g. 'it's less far because the brick is wide,' but they do recognize the equality of the distance AB and BA when there is a difference in level.

Nav (6;8). Two trees A and B: '*It's far.*—(A brick midway between them)—*It changes with the wall.*—How?—*It isn't as far now.* Why not?—*It's less wide.*—From one tree to the other?—*Yes, it's less far because the brick is wide.*'

B is raised: '*It's the same thing* from (A to B as B to A) *because it's the opposite way round.*' Reversal of direction here produces symmetry.

Other children at substage 2b realize that the distance between the two figures is not changed by the interposing of a screen or other object but do not appreciate the equality of the distance AB and BA, e.g. 'It's further going up' or 'It's difficult climbing' or 'It's longer going up.'

Gas (5;11). Interval lined with bricks; one brick removed: '*It's the same because you haven't moved either little man backwards or forwards.*—(A second brick removed.)—*It's the same,* (etc.).'

A and B facing each other on the same horizontal plane: '*They're both the same* (AB and BA).—(B is raised).—*The one on the mountain, it's nearer for him. It's going down. It's further for the one at the bottom. It's going up.*'

At *stage 3* (usually from 7 years on) children realize that the distance between the two stationary figures remains the same whatever is placed between them and that it is the same measured in either direction.

Stage 3. Lep (6;10). Screen introduced: 'Is it as far as it was or not?—*Yes, you see the little men are still on the same line. They haven't moved.*—(One brick interposed.)—*It comes back to the same. Bricks can't make the little men move!* (Door open or shut.)—'*One way they're looking at each other, the other way they can't see each other, but they're just as far.* (AB = BA)?—*Of course, it's the same thing.* (He laughs at the ridiculous question.)—And if I put this one up there?—*The man at the bottom must go this way and the other just the opposite. It's just as far!*'

Distance heralds the construction of a co-ordinate system and the organization of the spatial field by reference axes. These co-ordinates are not achieved until later (substage 3b). But the concept of invariant and symmetrical linear distances is the first step in that development, for it implies the recognition of space as a container, no longer as split into contents, or filled space, and absence of content, or empty space.

IV
Change of position and conservation of length

The Estimation of Length

The first of this group of experiments was planned to demonstrate the development of children's ability to estimate length and to show whether length was first thought of only in terms of two extremities or even in terms of the most distant point only. The children are shown a short straight wooden stick and a long undulating thread of plasticene. The ends of the plasticene are made to coincide with the ends of the wood and the objects are arranged side by side a few millimetres apart. The children are asked 'Are they the same length or is one longer than the other?' If they say they are the same, the children are asked to run their fingers along the stick and the plasticene and the question is then repeated. If they persist in saying they are the same, the question may be put in a form which draws attention to the path of movement. 'If there were two ants or two little men, and they walked along these lines which would they find longer?' Finally the 'snake' is straightened out upon which children readily admit that the 'snake' is now longer; the 'snake' is then twisted back to its original shape

18

and the question repeated. The majority of children below 4;6 answered at stage 1. They continued to regard the 'snake' and wood as being of the same length when the ends coincided, but the 'snake' was thought of as longer when straightened and as returning to the same length as the stick when twisted, i.e. they thought of length in terms of the two end-points only.

At substage 2a the children think the 'snake' is longer after they have thought of it in terms of movement, though not before, and at substage 2b, beginning at about 5;6, they respond correctly e.g. 'this one is longer because it is twisted.'

Comparison of Length

In this experiment the children were shown two 5-cm. straight sticks with their extremities facing each other. One of the sticks was then moved forward 1 or 2 cm. The subjects were asked in each position to say whether the sticks were of equal length or not. After the change of position children at the first stage say that the stick which has been moved is now longer, thinking only of the furthest extremity, e.g. 'That one is bigger because you moved it.' They are unable to consider both ends of the sticks at once or relate them to the sites which they occupy.

This response lasts into substage 2a, but at substage 2b there is a variety of intermediate responses resulting from progressive adjustments made by the children. For example, they say 'That one is longer there (to the right) and that one is longer there (to the left)' 'Then are they or aren't they the same length?' Hesitating: 'Yes'.

Children aged about 7 and upwards respond at the third stage, understanding that conservation is logically necessary —they bring into a single whole the stationary sites and the objects which are moved from one to another, e.g. 'It is always the same length. There's a little space there (difference between the leading extremities) and there's the same little space there' (difference between the trailing extremities). It is at this third stage only that conservation of length is secure.

There can be no conservation of length, any more than of distance, unless there is a reference system which provides a common medium for all objects, whether moving or stationary, and this in turn implies that there must be composition as between objects and their parts, and empty sites. The result, as was shown in Chapter III, is that notions of length and distance become comparable, because both are based on the appreciation of order and interval between sites. Such sites, whether empty or filled, form the essential framework of all metrics. The conservation of length, taken by itself, is similar to that of distance in that it leads both to measurement and to a comprehensive co-ordinate system.

V
Conservation and measurement of length

Conservation of length when an object changes position is not enough to allow understanding of measurement, as the process involves also subdivision and the construction of a unit of measurement. The following group of experiments sets out to show how children develop from an appreciation of conservation to the measurement of length.

1
Conservation of Length with Distortion of Shape

By way of introduction children may be presented with the following situation. Between twelve and sixteen matches are arranged in two parallel rows side by side so that their equality is obvious. One of the rows is then modified by the introduction of angles, thus, the matches may be arranged in a series of zigzags or at right-angles to one another, etc. Some of the matches may be broken to prevent numerical correspondence of the elements of each row. The subjects are asked whether the two lines are still the same length or, if that is too difficult, whether two ants walking along the rows would have the same distance to cover.

However, the crucial technique consists in asking the same questions using two strips of paper each 30 cm. long and about 1 cm. wide. The subject is first asked to assure himself that the two strips are identical in length. One of the strips is then cut first into two parts and later into several and then arranged in a variety of ways, the aim being to establish whether there is conservation of the overall length.

Questions about the strips of paper, like those about the rows of matches, may be asked either in terms of 'static' length or in terms of distances travelled. The answer is not always the same and the two languages should not be confused. The difficulty of using the first (static length) is to make the subject understand that what is required is the overall distance of the paper strip and not the rectilinear interval between its extremities, which obviously varies. The experimenter is therefore frequently compelled to use expressions which imply movement, though he should take care to gloss over the kinetic aspect and to use terms like 'road', 'path', etc.

At stage 1 and substage 2a conservation is lost when the strip is modified, intermediate responses are given at substage 2b and at stage 3 conservation is understood. At the first stage there is no conservation in either situation, but some children at substage 2a show the beginning of conservation when considering the matches, as they are influenced by the number of matches remaining the same, unless the change of arrangement is very great or one of the matches is broken. This failure is due to the lack of ability to consider together both subdivision and order or change of position. Stage 3 ($7\frac{1}{2}$–$8\frac{1}{2}$ years) responses show an ability to co-ordinate operations of subdivision and order or change of position, e.g. 'They're also the same length. You cut them but they're still the same size, only now they turn round.'

The ability to measure involves the *complete* fusion of

subdivision and change of position—an ability which comes a little later than the understanding of qualitative conservation. The next experiment is concerned with this development.

2
Measurement of lengths

The technique is a direct extension of that used already. The subject is again asked to judge between strips of paper in a variety of linear arrangements, involving right-angles, acute angles, etc., but these are now pasted on cardboard sheets. When he has given his replies, saying they are equal or that one is longer than the other, he is shown a number of movable strips and asked to verify his judgment: 'Have a look with this and see if you're right. Try and measure', etc. Later, he is given short strips of card 3 cm., 6 cm., sometimes 9 cm. long (these lengths corresponding with those of segments on the mounted strip).

The experimenter himself may apply the 3 cm. card two or three times along the mounted strip and explain these movements as the successive steps of 'a little man walking' and the subject is asked to finish himself what he has been shown. At stages 1 and substage 2a the structure of a unit of measurement is impossible. The steps procedure fails completely. The children do not see the necessity for using unit measures the same in each case or for placing the measuring card accurately. This follows from the children's lack of understanding of conservation—measurement involves an intermediary M which matches both A and B, but this can only be done by moving M from A to B and for these children the movement of M might involve a change in length. Similarly if several units M are used, a re-arrangement of them may make these children think that the total length has changed.

Substage 2b shows a beginning of understanding of conservation and the children respond to prompting, but do not spontaneously see the necessity for using units of the same size and are inclined to judge by 'looking'. Although stage 3 is reached in relation to qualitative conservation at about the age of $7\frac{1}{2}$ measurement with immediate insight instead of by trial and error is not achieved until about 8 or $8\frac{1}{2}$.

VI
Subdividing a straight line

In the previous experiment children were faced with lines already divided into segments and asked to compare them; in this experiment they are asked to locate a segment on a straight line equal to a segment given on another straight line. In order to do this various lengths of string are stretched in various positions between nails on a board, each string having a bead threaded on it. One of the beads is moved along one string and the subject is asked to make another bead travel the same length journey on its string. A blank wooden ruler, a stick, strips of plain paper, threads of various lengths and a pencil are available. During stage 1 and substage 2a the children are able to solve the problem if starting points and strings are in alignment, but as soon as this is not so they fail—if the strings are staggered they simply put their bead opposite the experimenter's and disregard the inequality of the journeys made. At substage 2b this problem is solved intuitively (by looking), but there is failure when the strings are of different lengths or not parallel nor in alignment, or when a child is asked to run its bead from the opposite end of the string. They attempt to measure but fail to see the need for accurate subdivision and for taking into account the point of departure as well as that of arrival. Moreover in all this the function of measurement is still only a secondary one. It is only used to verify a judgment reached on an intuitive basis, whether by visual estimate, or by using hands, etc.

At substage 3a the children measure the experimenter's bead's journey if the ruler is longer; failing this they improvise a suitable line of objects, e.g. the ruler, a pencil and a piece of paper. These are then transferred to the subject's string and the bead moved from one end to the other, i.e. only qualitative transitivity is achieved. Substage 3b (from about 8 years onward) is marked by the repeated application of a measuring rod to the first journey and using the measuring rod to find the position on the second string to which the bead must be moved, i.e. the first distance has been intellectually subdivided and transferred to the new position. Thus the notion of an elementary unit which may be applied indefinitely in a continuous series of changes of position involves the operational synthesis of subdivision and change of position. Conservation is now secure.

PART THREE

Rectangular co-ordinates, angles and curves

VII

Locating a point in two- or three-dimensional space

The experiments described so far show how children develop the ability to locate a point on a straight line, by measuring the distance from its origin to the point in question. The next experiments demonstrate the development of the ability to use rectangular co-ordinates and show how this depends on evolving a co-ordinate system.

To find a point in two dimensions the subject is given two sheets of plain white rectangular paper identical in size. One is placed at the top right-hand corner of the table and the second at the bottom left. On the first is a point P′ marked in red about halfway between the centre of the rectangle and its upper right-hand corner. The paper is semi-transparent and the subject is asked to mark a point on the second sheet in the same position as P′ on the first, so that if the second sheet is placed on top of the first, the two points will coincide. A two-decimetre ruler, stick, strips of paper and lengths of thread are provided.

In Chapter VI the bead was movable and its position was gained by movement from its point of origin. Here P′ is a stationary point, so that the subject does not know what to measure or where to measure from. The situation therefore constitutes an excellent medium for the study of spontaneous reactions to a problem which requires measurement in two dimensions. The problem is simply to make use of measurement in locating a point in an area, not to measure an area. Because the subject must orientate his own measurements, using the sides of rectangle S as axes, these observations enable us to determine, stage by stage, how measurement comes to be co-ordinated in two dimensions.

During stage 1 (until about 4 or 4;6) children make no use of the measuring material; they simply place their point by visual estimate. At substage 2a judgment is still visual; the measuring material may be used but only as an aid to perception. The visual estimate may be fairly accurate but may also be influenced by faulty logic and left and right positioning reversed etc.

During substage 2b children begin to measure, but make one measurement only, with the usual errors typical of this stage. Usually the ruler is laid obliquely from one corner of the rectangle or from some other prominent point, but this does not mean yet that both dimensions are taken into account, as little attention is paid to the actual angle of the ruler. Later in this stage, however, children begin to show an awareness of two dimensions by attempting to apply their ruler at an angle which takes account of both.

At stage 3 the children come to understand fully the need to take both dimensions into account. The final solution of the problem is achieved in two steps. At the beginning of substage 3a they start with a single oblique measurement, but show an increasing realization of the importance of the angle at which this is drawn. Gradually they decompose the latter into two separate measurements along different axes. However, although this discovery is crucial, it does not lead to the immediate co-ordination of length and width, but is followed by a great deal of trial-and-error behaviour.

30

At substage 3b (from around 9 years onward) the two measures are finally co-ordinated. Typical responses at this stage are—'Why did you measure like that? *To know where to put the point, in this direction and in that one too*—What if you simply took one measurement? *It wouldn't work. I'd be too high or too low or too far.*' or '*You've got to measure the height and width.*—Do you need two measurements?—*Yes, otherwise I'd put my point too low.*'

This behaviour is operational in character. The first situation is analysed in relation to a system of thought previously structured—a structure of co-ordinates in metric terms—and synthesized in the new position.

Measurement in three dimensions

The method used here is to present the subject with two identical open boxes. A short length of wire, nailed vertically to the base of one box, supports a bead. The subject is required to identify the position of the bead with reference to the sides of the box, these being higher than the bead itself. The other box is empty, but the subject is provided with another bead, a two-decimetre graduated ruler, strips of paper and lengths of wood, string, wire lengths, scissors to cut the wire and drawing pins with which to nail it. He is merely asked to produce an arrangement identical with that of the model, so that the second bead corresponds exactly with the first.

Once again at stage 1 and substage 2a visual estimates are considered adequate—'How do you know?—*I've guessed*—Isn't there something you could measure in there?—*No*—Why not?—*Because it's like that.*'

At substage 2b only one or two measurements are taken, by simple congruence and without metrical subdivision. Children at substage 3a eventually succeed in measuring in three

VIII
Angular measurement

1

Measuring Angles

In order to reproduce a diagram of an angle it is necessary to understand the relationship between the lengths of the arms of the angle and the distance between them, i.e. a one-many correspondence rather than the one-one correspondence between marked points on rectangular axes which must be understood in order to locate a point in space—either two- or three-dimensional. In order to investigate the development of this understanding, children were asked to reproduce a diagram showing two supplementary angles ADC and CDB.

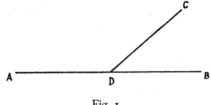

Fig. 1

They were not allowed to look at the drawing while actually reproducing it (it was on a table behind them) but were allowed to study and measure it as often as they wished. Rulers, strips of paper, string, cardboard triangles, compasses etc. were provided.

For children at stage 1 (up to 4–5 years) and substage 2a (up to about 6), visual judgment reigns supreme. No attempt is made at measuring either the lengths of lines or slopes. They fail to reproduce the diagram satisfactorily but see no use for the measuring apparatus.

Substage 2b (7–7½ years) shows the beginning of measurement either by hand or the use of a common measure longer than whatever is being measured—the slope is now taken into account but only by visual estimate—seeing that the drawing is composed of two lines the children do not even consider measuring anything but the two lines in the figure, e.g. AB or CD. They make such comments as 'It won't work. I don't know why not——I measured it right. Maybe your drawing is wrong!' or 'I measured that (AB) and that (CD) and that's all there is.'

Their attitude to the angle of incidence may seem extraordinary. Perception is fairly accurate, as is shown by the fact that subjects are critical of their own drawings after these are made. But although they can judge whether CD is correctly inclined to AB when their drawing is complete, they are quite unable to reproduce the slope of the model, let alone measure it.

As has already been described, children at substage 3a (7½–8½ years) are able to co-ordinate subdivision and change of position—this makes it possible to measure the lines AD or DB or both. Sometimes they begin by inserting D by inspection, but they quickly go on to measuring. However, the solution to the reproduction of the correct slope still eludes them—they are aware of slope and try to reproduce it by holding the ruler steady during transfer from model to repro-

34

The technique used is as before, but what children are asked to reproduce this time is a drawing of a triangle. At stage 1 they cannot copy a triangle at all, and even at substage 2a no measurement is attempted. Thus Ta (6;5) after a struggle produces a triangle which is quite different from the model, and says *'I've tried it all and it won't work.*—Why not?—*I don't know.*—Couldn't you do it better by using a ruler?—*No, because the line I have to draw is not straight* (indicating the perimeter of the triangle), *but the ruler is a straight line.'*

One-dimensional measurement of each side begins at substage 2b (around $7\frac{1}{2}$ years), but the children fail to reproduce their inclinations. As in the problem of angular measurement, they do not realize that this demands an additional measurement. They are therefore at a loss to know where and how to make the sides meet and often fail to make them meet at all. They see no opportunity for measurement of anything but the three lines in the model. They attempt to account for their failure as being the result of having measured the sides in the wrong order—not seeing that this has no significance.

At substage 3a ($8\frac{1}{2}$–9 years) the children again try to transfer the slope of the ruler and combine this with a trial-and-error approach to the problem of making the sides meet. Towards the end of this substage, children no longer try to maintain a constant slope with their ruler but simply adjust the three measurements to one another by trial and error. There is, however, a growing precision about the way this is done, which begins to foreshadow level 3b.

At that level (9–10 years) children immediately decompose the triangle to arrive at a height perpendicular to one of the sides in addition to a length for each side. Thus all the relevant dimensions are ascertained in a systematic manner without trial and error. (See diagram, dotted lines BK' or BK.)

At stage 4 (10–11 years) they spontaneously introduce construction lines which did not appear before and usually seem to prefer to establish K″C, which lies outside the original triangle.

K″ lies on the prolongation of AB where it meets the perpendicular from C. This construction does not argue a different co-ordination from that of level 3b, but it argues a greater freedom from the limitations of what is perceptually given, and as such it is typical of the beginnings of formal thought.

Fig. 3

Measurement of an irregular polygon

In order to check these findings, a number of children at the various levels were presented with an irregular polygon, and asked to copy it. The figure is unlike any they are likely to encounter in their school work, but it can be decomposed as a number of triangles (Fig. 3). The responses agree well with those given in previous tasks, measuring a triangle or supplementary angles, although complete success appears somewhat later.

3
The sum of the angles of a triangle

If measurement implies a complex operational co-ordination, then the stages in measuring angles and triangles should have a counterpart in the development of reasoning about metrical relations, which are founded on the understanding of measurement. The fact that the sum of the angles of a triangle is always 180° suggests an interesting technique for analysing the whole genetic sequence from the construction of measurement to mathematical reasoning about metric relations. In presenting the problem, care was taken to avoid such verbal formulae as 'the sum of its angles', and instead of using the abstract notion of 180° we spoke of a semi-circle, which can be seen or envisaged intuitively.

The use of a concrete mode of presentation made it a simple matter to put the problem to children of all ages from 4 or 5 to 11 or 12, in order to analyse the responses at each of the levels which figure in the measurement of angles and triangles. The child is simply asked to predict what the angles of a triangle will look like if cut with scissors and rearranged in the shape of a half moon. He may be shown that in this or that instance they form a semi-circle and the enquiry is pursued to see whether he will generalize the solution to differently shaped triangles.

In the actual experiments children are presented with various triangles, some with their angles already cut into sectors and others not. They are asked questions about the shape which will be formed if all the angles are removed and reassembled together. In some cases two of the angles are put together and the children are asked what will be produced when the third is added to them. Rearrangement of the angles is sometimes suggested to discover whether the children appreciate that this will not affect the sum. Finally a very elongated triangle is introduced to see how far the findings can be generalized.

These techniques gave rise to the following results: At levels 1 and 2a (up to about 6 years) children cannot abstract the angles as such nor foresee their sum. To them the orginal angles are 'roofs' and their re-arrangement is a 'half-moon' and the two are utterly heterogeneous. When considering their re-arrangement, they concentrate on their number and ignore their angular shapes. Even after seeing for themselves that their sum is a semi-circle, they do not generalize this result. Children even fail to see that simply altering the order of their arrangement will not affect their sum, i.e. there is no conservation.

38

At substage 2b (6–7 years) they realize that the semi-circle will stay when the angles are changed round, but they are not sure that the angles of a different triangle will also add up to the same thing. Just as children at substage 3a become aware of the importance of slope in angular measurement, so at this stage they begin to consider the angles of the triangle separately and the effect of uniting them. However, generalization is often slow and liable to fail when children are presented with a triangle which has one very acute angle or one very obtuse, or a right-angled triangle; their attention is apt to be centred on the arresting angle and they temporarily neglect the other two. Thus the complementary relation between the angles of a triangle is not generalized once and for all, but is a finding which is slowly reached by comparing each fresh triangle with those previously encompassed.

At substage 3b (8–10 years) children recognize the law as universally applicable but not as logically necessary, whereas only at stage 4 (10–12 years) do children begin to see the logical reason for the geometrical law.

It is difficult to find an exact criterion for the boundary between substage 3b and stage 4. Needless to say, we cannot expect all children at 10 to 12 to demonstrate the theorem (and subjects who had tackled the problem in their school work were omitted from the investigation). All that we can look for is an indication of when 'always' becomes 'necessarily', which means that a law which is generalized intuitively is seen as governed by necessary reason.

The examples given by Piaget show that these children do not know in advance the theorem which deals with the sum of the angles of a triangle. Yet they discover unaided that, whatever the angles taken separately, their sum is constant and they realize that this relationship is a necessary one. It is clear from the records that if they see the relationship as necessary, it is because they look on the angles of a triangle as forming a system of complementary parts, and, going beyond

IX

Two problems of geometrical loci:
the straight line and the circle

The study of loci is interesting because the subject cannot construct such figures without making a generalization based on an action or operation which is indefinitely repeated. This principle is as fundamental in geometrical reasoning as in arithmetic. In the study of loci a general principle of reasoning is being analysed, just as in the preceding study of the sum of the angles of a triangle.

Two relations are considered: (1) the locus of points equidistant from two points A and B; (2) the locus of all points equidistant from a given point.

The first problem is studied by one of three techniques: (1) We imagine a boy standing at A and another at B; where shall we put a target such as an agate marble (which children use as a 'jack' when playing marbles) so as to be at the same distance from either boy? It is made clear, if necessary, that all possible positions are to be indicated.

(2) There is a tree at A and another at B. Where can you stand so as to be at the same distance from either tree?

(3) For the youngest subjects the experimenter stands or sits on the far side of the table: the child is handed a number of

marbles and asked to put them the same distance from himself and the experimenter.

The problem of rectilinear locus is extended with the older subjects to cover equidistance from a number of points, A, B, C, D and A', B', C', D' where A, B, C, D are on a straight line and A', B', C', D' on another straight line at right-angles to it and at corresponding distances along it.

The second problem introduces curvilinear measurement. The children are asked to show where a series of children should stand (or where a set of marbles should be placed) in order to be the same distance (or 'just as far') from the above 'target'.

At stage 1, until the age of about 5, there is no notion of distance as being stable, as we have seen; consequently the idea of equidistance has little meaning and these subjects indicate a point at random for the solution of the first problem and merely arrange the marbles round the central one, in the second case, with no regard for distance.

Stage 2 (from 5 to 7, on the average) falls as usual into two substages and these correspond to quite distinct levels in the construction of 'loci'. In the problem of the circle children at substage 2a (5–6) simply arrange the marbles either in a row or else in an irregular ring around the central one, without any attempt to measure from this. As regards the first problem, they are usually only able to find one solution, i.e. the mid-point of the line joining A and B, estimated perceptually, but fairly accurately. In the case of the paired points on lines at right-angles they are only able to consider two of the points, e.g. A.A' or else produce irregular intervals between the various marbles.

On the other hand, during substage 2b, generalization begins to appear, though only as a kind of simple empirical repetition of the right behaviour. Thus in the case of the first problem children presently discover the point of equi-distance between two others and then show an inkling of the

42

locus (by placing one marble behind another in a continuous line which follows the same direction). There are occasional errors in equidistance due to over-emphasis on continuing in a chosen direction without any thought given to symmetry, e.g. Dub (6;8) arranging boys to be equidistant from two trees; '*In the middle.*—And the next one?—*Underneath* (maintaining the equidistance).—And the next?—*Underneath that*—And after that?—*It continues* (putting down a few at equal intervals and fairly close together)—How far?—*Up to the edge of the paper.*—Would they still be the same distance from both of the trees?—*Yes.*—And if we had many sheets of paper?—*We could go on putting children.*' Thus Dub accepts the suggestion but his generalization extends only to one side.

Other children at this stage manage to achieve generalization in both directions and in some cases to move towards continuity, first by narrowing the intervals between marbles (or points), and later by interpolating others in these spaces.

Throughout stage 3 (from 7–8 onward) the children start with the correct presupposition, one which makes it possible to generalize the relation of equidistance. There is never any doubt that what is sought is a series of points having certain characteristics in common. The most important achievement at this stage is reasoning by recurrence. The child simply determines a few points in the series and immediately concludes that all points on the circle or straight line must have the same property.

X

Representation of circles, mechanical and composite curves

The previous chapter studied one way in which the simplest curve, the circle, can be constructed. The present chapter sets out to study how far children can learn to understand another way of constructing not only circles, but also more complex curves, such as spirals and cycloids (the so-called mechanical curves). This other way is by following paths of movement. As applied to spirals, however, it involves two reference systems instead of one and introduces problems which—like that of the sum of the angles of a triangle—cannot be finally solved before the level of formal operations. If a cylinder is revolved while an ant moves along its length, keeping to whatever portion is the uppermost, the total movement so described will be a spiral. Similarly if a red disc or lantern is attached to the rim of a cartwheel in motion the disc or lantern would describe a cycloid curve. In order to predict either of these the horizontal and rotational movements must both be taken into account. This is more difficult than the loci problems as it requires the synthesis of two separate paths.

The group of experiments is introduced by an investigation into the children's ability to construct a curve derived from simple rotary movement (a circle) or from the composition of two simultaneous movements.

Q.1. A wooden disc is made to move around its own axis, the disc being pinned to a sheet of paper by a needle passing through its centre. A pencil is fastened to a point on its circumference. The child is asked to predict what kind of a line the pencil will draw when the disc is rotated. This experiment is followed by variants, when a square or triangle is used instead of a disc.

Q.2. The disc is stood upright and made to roll along a table while the pencil draws a path on a sheet of paper perpendicular to the table top. Prediction of the shape of the line is asked for when the pencil is fastened: (a) to the circumference, (b) to the centre and (c) to a point anywhere between the circumference and the centre of the disc. The problem involves the three possible forms of a cycloid: (a) a series of hoops, (b) truncated hoops and (c) a straight line (the limiting case).

Q.3. A wooden cylinder is turned horizontally about its axis. An ant which has walked through an inkblot is said to walk along the roller. The child is asked to predict the path: (a) when the roller stays stationary and the pencil (or ant) moves forward (a straight line), (b) when the ant (or pencil) is stationary but the roller rotates (a circle), and (c) when both move simultaneously (spiral). In the last case the relative speeds may be varied.

Q.4. This involves the reconstruction of composite movement but in a simpler form than in the previous question. The apparatus consists of a model snail fitted with a pencil which can be pulled by means of a wire along a slot cut parallel to the shorter edges of a rectangular board while the board moves in a line parallel to its longer edges. The child is asked to predict the path taken by the snail. The correct prediction would be an oblique line where the board and the snail move at the same speed, but relative speeds may be varied according to the requirements of the situation.

45

Q.5. Further to the ant and cylinder problem, the child is asked to predict the path of the ant if it moved along the axis of rotation, i.e. does he realize that a straight line pivoting about its own axis remains a straight line?

Throughout stage 1 children are unable to imagine a movement before its occurrence and simply make a pencil mark or draw the object at rest. At substage 2a children begin to imagine curves of movement, but in question 1 are unable to differentiate the curve described by movement from the outline of the object itself, e.g. when asked what shape path the pencil attached to the triangle will produce they draw a triangle.

In attempting questions 2, 3 and 4 these children are unable to differentiate curves produced by simple movements from curves produced by composite movements. In answering question 2 these children draw a circle or a series of circles instead of a cycloid; for question 3 they produce a straight line instead of a spiral; for question 4 a vertical line instead of an oblique. At substage 2b, question 1 is answered correctly, the ability to differentiate between a static shape and a path of movement having developed. The answers to questions 2, 3 and 4 produce a number of interesting compromises. Thus, although the cycloid is always represented as a series of circles in juxtaposition, these may be drawn as ellipses in order to co-ordinate the movement of the disc on its own axis with its change of position (displacement) relative to the table. The spiral is often shown as an oblique line, which is a compromise between the forward movement of the ant on the cylinder and the rotary movement of the cylinder itself.

During stage 3 (beginning at 7–8) children gradually reach the correct solutions after trial and error—at substage 3a some failure continues, but in substage 3b all questions are answered correctly after some hesitation and error. At stage 4 (formal operations), which may begin at 9 but is usually later and may be imperfect even for adults, there is no hesitation or trial and error.

46

PART FOUR

Areas and Solids

This part describes the development of notions of area and volume which depend upon the mathematical multiplication of measurements rather than the logical operations necessary to locate a point in space or construct an angle or path of movement. The investigation aims to relate the stages of development of understanding of metric co-ordinate systems to the development of the understanding of area and volume.

XI

The conservation and measurement of an area and subtracting smaller congruent areas from larger congruent areas

1

Subtracting smaller congruent areas from larger congruent areas

At what stage do children understand that if two equal parts are substracted from two equal wholes the remainders will also be equal? If that does not seem self-evident to them at a given age, when does it come to be seen? That implies the notion of the conservation of an area if its parts are re-arranged. While the immediate questions deal with subtracting or adding parts, the underlying purpose is to study conservation—both of parts and wholes. The ability to analyse a whole in this way is a prerequisite to measurement because when measuring an area we assume, as we do for all measurement, that partial units are conserved and can be composed in a variety of ways to form invariant wholes.

In order to answer the above questions children were faced with two identical rectangular sheets of green cardboard which were described as meadows with grass for cows to eat. They were enabled to realize the identity of the fields by putting them side by side to make sure. A model cow and farmer were then introduced and the children had no difficulty in appreciating that each cow had the same amount of grass to eat. They were then told that one farmer decided to build a house on his meadow—a model about 1 cm. by 2 cm. or a cube or wooden brick to stand for the farmhouse being placed on one meadow. All the children asked were able to say at once that the cow in the field with the house had less grass to eat than that in the field without the house. When an identical house was placed on the second field the children all agreed that each cow had the same amount of grass. However, one house was placed centrally in the field and the other rather near one corner, and the procedure was continued by adding further identical houses to each field—those in one field being distributed at random with 'grass' space between them, those in the second field being placed adjacent to one another in a continuous line. Younger children were increasingly deceived by the arrangement, not seeing that two houses widely spread from one another occupy the same space as two identical houses closed up into one corner. Some children maintained the sameness of the grass area for a small number of houses and lost it for a large number, while older children maintained it throughout.

It was found difficult to pursue the enquiry with children at stage 1. At substage 2a (5–6 years) children are obviously interested, yet they refuse to admit that the remaining areas are equal, often at the very first pair of houses. At 2b we find a complete range of intermediate responses: up to a certain number of houses the subject recognizes that the remaining grass areas are equal; beyond that number the perceptual configurations are too different. Thus a typical comment at this substage expresses the conflict between perceptual impression and intellectual judgment: 'It's really the same, but there's still more space here.'

At stage 3, however, and even at level 3a (usually at $7\frac{1}{2}$ but sometimes as early as $6\frac{1}{2}$–7 years) children recognize that areas were equal, or that there was 'the same amount of room' (the formulation being similar to that used in section 1). In order to dissociate these two aspects and avoid any verbal misunderstanding, the experimenter took 96 little wooden cubes or a few sheets of cardboard which covered the rectangle exactly and asked the child whether these would exactly cover the shape as well. (The cubes recall the 'houses' of section 1, but their number was purposely made larger so that the child should be unable to count them.) However, this technique led to the strange result that some children correctly predicted that the same number of cubes could be used to cover the second figure without necessarily admitting that the areas were equal. This rather paradoxical finding gives a useful pointer to the way in which children develop the notion of area.

Because the results of method 1 were not unequivocal, method 2 was also used, in which the child was simply shown two rectangles recognized as congruent and the experimenter then cut a portion off one and moved it to another part of the same figure. Thus he cut the rectangle diagonally in half and put the two sections together in the shape of a triangle, or he cut off the four corners and put them against the sides to produce an irregular polygon, etc. Any congruent figures could be used instead of rectangles, if desired. The question was always: 'Are these the same size? Is there the same amount of room?' etc. These were varied and repeated to be certain that the answer was a judgment of area as such.

At levels 1 and 2a children believe that the area changes with change of shape and neither can they measure areas, as they lack conservation of the movable middle term. Children at level 2b gradually come to make a number of true judgments but are unable to generalize though there is some beginning of the ability to measure. At level 3a ($6\frac{1}{2}$–7 years) children understand the conservation of area when the parts are re-arranged or shape is altered (though only for surfaces within a given perimeter and not extending to the complementary areas outside). Middle terms are now used as a common measure, but the concept of a unit of measure is not understood—the middle terms may be of different size, yet all are counted as equal.

The typical responses at the various substages are:

2a 'No, it's not the same any more because you've cut it.'
   'It's bigger here because you've made a turning.'

2b *That makes it less.*—Why?—*Because it's not the same any more.*—What if I put it back?—*Oh yes! It is the same.* —And this way? (one square cut in pieces and spread out) *It's the same.*

3a 'It's the same thing, there's the same amount of space.'
   'Yes, it's the same space, because if you put them together it would be the same.'

Thus it may be seen that the operational conservation of area appears at the same time as that of distance and length —a whole is conceived of as an invariant whole whatever the disposition of its parts.

Conservation of an area outside a closed perimeter

The apparatus for this experiment is similar to that of the first experiment in this group. Two fields and two cows, but instead of sets of identical houses being built on each, two potato patches (brown cards), one a complete square and the other an identical square cut into movable sections. When the sameness of the areas involved has been verified, the experimenter alters the shape of the second plot by separating the sections (which are not all alike). The child is thereupon asked: (1) 'Is there the same space for potatoes on both fields?' (Do the two areas remain equal although their distribution is different?) (2) 'Is there still as much grass for each of the two cows?' (Do complementary areas remain equal as well?).

Up to and including substage 2a (about 7 years) there is no conservation of either the interior or the complementary areas (potato-patches or field)—some children even thought both areas had increased when the second patch was broken up, i.e. more room for potatoes and for more grass! At level 3a the interior area only is conserved but at substage 3b conservation of both areas is understood.

Measurement of Areas

Measurement by Super-position. Children are faced with the problem of comparing the sizes of a right-angled triangle and a somewhat larger irregular figure. (Fig. 4).

Fig. 4

They are provided with a number of measuring cards, consisting of square, rectangles and triangles, enough or nearly enough to cover each figure.

Children at stage 1 and substage 2a fail to see any use for the measuring cards. Even after they have been shown how to cover each figure separately the relationships involved elude them. Their judgment is based on perceptual considerations and uninfluenced by logical ones. Even after covering both shapes—the irregular shape having needed all the units of measurement and the triangular only some, they are still capable of saying that the triangle is larger. Children are able at this substage to apply congruent single shapes one to another, but when one of the areas is divided the congruence is lost. Similarly, a number of sections covering a whole are deemed to be less than that whole as soon as they are moved.

During substage 2b children gradually discover that if fewer measuring cards are required to cover one of the figures than to cover the other, the first must be smaller. The children need encouraging to use the common measure and are not convinced of the significance of its use, e.g. 'That one is bigger (irregular shape) because I needed all the cards for it, but I didn't on that one (triangle).' The irregular shape was then compared with the collection of smaller measuring cards. 'The little bits make more. Oh no! It's the same.' There is better conservation. In other words the composition of parts within a whole and the composition of position and changes of position are more co-ordinated.

The use of the common measure and the recognition of its transferability are immediate at stage 3. Nevertheless we still find two substages—at 3a the need is not realized for all the units of measurement to be identical. But at 3b children understand the notion of a unit and so they take the size of the measuring elements into account.

Measurement by unit iteration

The difference between this experiment and the previous one is that in this the child is given only one unit of measurement and asked to compare the sizes of various figures.

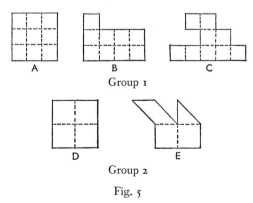

Group 1

Group 2

Fig. 5

The cards are plain white without lines.

To measure group 1 the child is given a unit square and a pencil. To measure group 2 there is a choice of three measures. A square which is one quarter of D, a rectangle worth two such squares and a triangle equivalent to one such square cut diagonally.

At stage 1 and substage 2a perceptual considerations reign supreme. Even after having been shown how to mark off unit squares and count them and finding that nine squares can be drawn on each of the first figures, one may still be considered bigger than another. Subdivision into squares clearly has no operational significance for these children—they lack notions of conservation and of additive composition. Each of the unit squares has a unique value by virtue of its position so that it cannot be compared with squares in other positions.

At level 2b the children all eventually convince themselves that A and B (in group 1) are equal in area because each is composed of nine squares. But the same children all persist in treating squares and triangles as equivalent units when comparing D and E. Thus, taken as a whole, the level shows an improvement in the composition of subdivisions and also in that of positions as given and changes in these positions, but the two articulations are not fully co-ordinated, and, above all, the notion of a metric unit is still unformed.

Levels 3a and 3b show first the above co-ordination and then the synthesis of the two articulations into an operational measuring unit. Children at level 3a all count the squares and triangles as equivalent units until their error is pointed out. The mastery of the common measure is achieved but not as a single scheme of unit operation; this must wait until stage 3b when children measure area by the successive application of a unit of area inside a larger area. The direct transition from length to area by arithmetical multiplication is not understood until stage 4 (8–9 years).

XII
Subdivision of areas and the concept of fractions

This section investigates further the construction of part-whole relations and the development of notions of fractions. The material consists of a number of clay 'cakes' of various shapes which the children, whose ages range from 4 to around 7, are asked to share equally between an increasing number of dolls. Many children experience difficulty in dividing the clay, so they are asked to cut various paper circles, rectangles and squares using scissors, starting with division into thirds and being provided with a pencil to mark the position of the cuts before making them if they wish. Another possible variant is to provide sticks to put along the proposed boundaries before drawing or cutting. Finally the children are asked if all the pieces they have cut would make up a whole cake if put together again, or 'Supposing we stuck all these bits together again, how many whole cakes would we have?'

During stage 1 (up to around 4;0 or 4;6) children still find real difficulty in dividing a cake in two halves; the earliest solution is no more than a general fragmentation, that is, the children do not stop at two. Next we find either that each doll is given an approximately equal share, but only a small one, leaving a large part undivided, or else the entire cake is shared out but in unequal portions. In the latter event we occasionally find a child dividing the cake into three because he confuses the number of cuts with the number of parts (cutting the cake twice gives three parts).

There are in fact seven characteristics of a fraction which need to be considered:

1. There must be a divisible whole, one which is composed of separable elements. Very young children (around 2 years) regard the cake as a single indivisible object and, in view of its closed and continuous shape, they refuse altogether to cut it. At $2\frac{1}{2}$ or 3, these inhibitions are overcome and children are ready to share or to cut out, but now the act of cutting makes the object lose it character of wholeness.

2. A fraction implies a determinate number of parts, i.e. the sharing presupposes a correspondence between parts and recipients. The youngest children who cut the cake at all forget the need for this correspondence and produce any number of fragments.

3. Subdivision into fractions is exhaustive, i.e. there is no remainder. Children who remember the first two characteristics only and forget this cut two pieces from the cake and leave the rest saying, when asked, 'That's nothing' or 'That's for nobody', or 'That's the table'.

4. There is a fixed relationship between the number of parts into which a continuous whole is to be divided and the number of intersections. But young children think of one cut in conjunction with one part, so that they are apt to make two cuts in order to obtain one half for each of two dolls. They thus unexpectedly get three parts, though if they had wanted to divide the cake into three, they could not have done so.

5. The concept of an arithmetical fraction implies that all the parts are equal. In attempting to equalize parts the first-stage children leave undistributed remainders.

6. True fractions are both parts of an original whole and are

58

also wholes in their own right. This is clearly beyond the understanding of first-stage children.

7. Since fractions of an area are relative to the whole from which they are drawn, that whole remains invariant, i.e. the sum of fractions equals the original whole. First-stage children do not appreciate this necessary conservation.

The sharing into halves is achieved at the beginning of stage 2 $(4-4\frac{1}{2})$ where the objects are small and their shape simple, but if the size is increased or the shape considerably altered, e.g. very long, thin rectangle or more complex shapes, like zig-zags, triangles, etc. these children continue to fail.

In any case substage 2a children are unable to cut the cake into three equal pieces when asked. Either they just cut small portions from the whole (though now they often divide the remainder again into three); or, being now able to divide into two equal shares, they try to arrive at third shares that way, sometimes by a second subdivision into two—the extra quarter which that leaves them with they apportion as best they can.

During substage 2b (6–7 years) the problem is gradually solved and trisection is immediate at stage 3 $(6\frac{1}{2}-8$ years$)$. Indeed, even at substage 3a, children are able not only to trisect but also to divide into fifths or sixths. But the latter power is not yet clear-cut. Trisection into three approximately equal parts takes place without trial and error, but this is still needed to achieve division into fifths or sixths. Only at substage 3b (9–10 years) is such division carried out with the same assurance as trisection.

The facts studied in this chapter show that the notions of fractions and even of halves presuppose a qualitative or intensive substructure. Any parts which are being considered must first be grasped as integral parts of a whole that can be both divided and brought together again, before they can be equated with one another and thus transformed into fractions. But this process of equating of the parts, once they are grasped

59

as such, is much easier than to master the operations of sub-division, and therefore the concept of a fraction follows closely on that of a part. It arises through the simple process of bringing the parts into relation with one another, and this becomes possible as soon as they are subordinated to the whole.

XIII
Doubling an area or volume

The operations considered so far in relation to areas and volumes were all capable of being handled on a purely logical plane, that is, without numerical multiplication. Frequently the elements and relations involved were such as could be expressed in quantitative terms, but the problem of calculating an area in such terms has not yet been studied. This in fact introduces a new element which goes beyond the purely logical operations envisaged up to now; a rectangle measuring 2×3 linear units gives six *square* units. Thus even where the conservation and measurement of areas was being expressly considered, the questions put to the children were such that they only needed to apply ready-made units of area (squares, rectangles, equilateral triangles, etc.); they did not have to calculate the area as a function of linear measurements. Similarly in the chapter which dealt with the subdivision of areas, the process consisted in dividing whole areas into partial ones, so that the units involved were all square units and the numerical relation between area and length of side was irrelevant.

The problem now to be studied is that of the relation

between measurement of the sides of a figure and that of its area or volume. This usually proves harder than the problems previously considered and is not fully solved until children reach the age when geometry is normally introduced into the school curriculum, that is, until stage 4 and the beginning of formal operations. But nevertheless the stages of their progress towards the right solution can be analysed in a way which reduces associations with the classroom to a minimum. It is in fact possible to pinpoint the underlying operational mechanisms without stressing the final answer in its numerical form. Thus subjects are simply asked to double an area or volume. No precise determination is called for, since that would involve not only arithmetical multiplication and division, but square roots and cube roots as well. All that is aimed at—and this should be relatively easy—is to find the answer to the following question: how does the subject establish a relation between length of the sides and area or volume, and how is he led to substitute mathematical multiplication for the merely logical manipulation of the relations concerned?

First, as a preliminary test, the child is asked to draw a line twice as long as a given line (2 or 3 cm.), pencil, ruler and strips of paper being provided.

He is then asked to draw a square twice as large as a given square (3 × 3 cm.), i.e. a square field with the same amount of grass for each of two cows as this has for one.

As a counter experiment the first field is fitted over the corner of the one drawn and the child asked whether the uncovered part of his field really contains as much grass as the covered part. If necessary the uncovered portion may be cut and the child told to regroup the segments to see whether they will cover the first field. But drawing and construction are insufficient; the child is asked also to choose out of 4 squares with sides of 4, 4·25, 5 and 6 cm. one which he thinks double the 3-cm.-square model.

Next we go on to a similar enquiry dealing with circular

and triangular fields and with an irregular field consisting of a 4-cm. square less a 2·5-cm. square removed from one corner.

For doubling the cube no drawing is required and the child is simply shown a model which is a 3-cm. cube together with a range of larger cubes of which the largest is a 6-cm. cube. The child is asked to choose which cube will hold just twice as much as the model and the countercheck consists in asking the child how many unit-volumes will go into the cube he has chosen. The initial cube (or unit cube) is filled with sand or with little wooden cubes and then emptied into the one chosen by the subject to help him understand the question.

At stage 1 the experiment is ruled out altogether. At stage 2 (from about 4–7½) doubling is a matter of a slight but arbitrary increase in size. This is true even of doubling a length of 2 or 3 cm.; instead of re-applying the straight line, using it as a unit of measurement, the subject merely draws another straight line which projects a little farther. Squares or cubes are chosen at random.

At substage 3a children either juxtapose two areas or volumes, overlooking the requirement of shape, or they simply double all the dimensions—succeeding with the straight-line only. Substage 3b is an interesting turning point, but the problem of doubling an area or volume is still not solved operationally—efforts at solution are still empirical. The 3a procedures are still applied, but seen to be unsatisfactory. The child thereupon tries various other ways of establishing a relation between the length of side and the area, but without real success. The same holds for the triangles and circles; he doubles the diameter or raises its value arbitrarily, but at the same time he is aware of the discrepancy between the product of his effort and the doubled area which he wants. Doubling a cube is solved in an approximate fashion, but with only some beginning of composition.

The crucial stage is the transition from 3b to 4. Children at level 3b have difficulty in moving from linear dimensions to measures of area or capacity. However, multi-dimensional measurement is now possible and suffices to shatter the child's former belief in direct proportionality between the lengths of boundary lines and the areas or volumes which they enclose. But he has still to grasp the actual relation between lengths and two- or three-dimensional continua. This comes only at stage 4, where it overlaps with the specific academic instruction directed to such problems. However, if a child begins to understand that the calculation of an area or volume involves mathematical multiplication, he can up to a point construct such a relation for himself.

Thus the following examples of stage 4 may be noted: Schnei (11;7) begins drawing a square with sides twice as long as the original (a 6-cm. square for a 3-cm. square), but halfway there he stops and says: '*No, that would give me an area of 36 sq. cm. That's wrong.* (He considers the matter carefully and says at last:) *I must make the side 4·5 cm.*—How did you work that out?—*This is 9 sq. cm., so twice that is 18 sq. cm. Then I divided that by 4 and that gives me 4·5 cm.* (He thinks a little and then adds: *No, that would be too much. I've got to make it 4 cm.* (an empirical guess)'.)

Ray (12;10) tries making the side 6 cm. in order to get a square twice the size of a 4-cm. square: '*I make each side 2 cm. longer because that's half four. I know how to work out an area:* $4 \times 4 = 16$ *sq. cm. A square twice as big would be 32 sq. cm. Mine is* $6 \times 6 = 36$ *sq. cm. So it's wrong.* $36 - 32 = 4$ *sq. cm. You ought really to take a little square of 4 sq. cm. off one corner.*— But it's got to stay a square.—*Let's try 5·5 cm. That's 30·25 sq. cm. so it's not enough. Try 5·6.*' In the end he produces a square of about 5·7 cm.

These solutions are obviously influenced by schooling, but even so are not perfect, and for that very reason enable us to see how the child's own mind works and carries him *towards* the right understanding and the correct answer.

XIV
The conservation and measurement of volume

Although area and volume are closely related geometrically, the question of volume raises many problems of its own. It is intimately bound up, psychologically, with physical objects, and indeed we cannot ask children about the conservation of volume without introducing physical objects like bricks or cubes filled with sand, etc. A question which thus arises is how far the understanding of conservation of volume can develop through the qualitative appreciation of the conservation of a given amount of substance. Or does this understanding have to wait for the construction of a spatial continuum and the notion of space as such, whether occupied or unoccupied?

To investigate these questions, children are shown a solid block 4 cm. high on a square base 3 cm. × 3 cm., so that its volume is 36 cubic cm. They are told that the block is a house on an island and asked to build a new house with exactly as much room as the old on other islands of different size or shape, with bases measuring 2 × 2 cm., 3 × 2 cm., 1 × 2 cm., 1 × 1 cm. and 3 × 4 cm. The problem thus consists in reproducing the volume of the first block while altering its form to comply with the above different bases. The child must moreover construct the new houses out of little cubes of 1 cubic cm. each.

Various subsidiary techniques are also introduced. The child is asked to reproduce the model with different sizes and shapes of bricks. He is also asked to compare these with one another, two at a time, and to say whether there is as much wood in each of them. Or again he may be handed a large block of wood and asked to find another with the same volume out of a number of alternatives which differ in shape.

Finally the experimenter starts from the 'house' which (with or without help) the child has reconstructed out of his unit-cubes, and now proceeds himself to build various constructions on different bases out *of the same cubes*. The child watches this and is then asked; (a) whether there is the same room, or more, or less, in the new house as in the old, and (b) whether one could use the self-same cubes which now make up the new house in order to re-make one like the original and exactly the same size.

Moreover, as a check on the results of the above techniques the problem of the conservation of volume when a solid object is immersed in water was also introduced. The child is shown a set of 1 cm. cubes which are then put at the bottom of a bowl of water. The experimenter builds a block out of 36 units ($3 \times 3 \times 4$) while the subject notes how the level of the water rises in the bowl. He is then asked if he thinks the level will change if the arrangement of the bricks is modified, by making constructions of $2 \times 1 \times 18$ or $2 \times 2 \times 9$, etc. This makes it easy to question him concerning three different kinds of volume; internal volume, or the conservation of the 36 bricks, volume as occupied space, being the amount of 'room' taken up by the 36 bricks in the water, and finally, the complementary volume, i.e. the volume of the water. Both the last two volumes are measured by the level of the water, and where the subject recognizes their conservation, this is shown by the fact that he anticipates that the level remains unaltered. In addition to questions about the level, the child may be asked whether the bricks will continue to 'take up the same amount of space in the water' or whether 'there will be as much room for the water as before', etc.

At stage 1 the foregoing techniques are impracticable. Stage 2 usually lasts from about 4;6 until between 5 and 7. At substage 2a children think in terms of one dimension only and usually stop building when their house has reached the same height as the model irrespective of the size of the base; at substage 2b the children begin to vary the height of their own models in relation to the size of the base—there is a shift from concentration on one dimension only to relationships between dimensions, but this is qualitative only and never goes far enough. Throughout stage 2 there is no conservation —if a group of bricks is sufficiently transformed in arrangement the children think that the 'amount of room' has changed. They may even say 'It's the same bricks but there is more room.'

Stage 3 begins around the age of 6;6 or 7;6 and continues until 11 or 12. Children at substage 3a work out the relations between the three dimensions (although to begin with they cannot handle more than two, and the third is progressively adjusted to these two), but without measuring. When faced with problems of transformation in the shapes of the houses, they cannot at this stage dissociate the three notions of height, shape and volume. So they now build a taller house on a small island, but are still unable to determine how much taller it should be, because they cannot make the differences equal and compensatory by using metrical decomposition and re-composition.

As regards the conservation of volume, this exists only in relation to 'interior volume'; in other words, the subject recognizes the invariance of the amount of matter which is contained within the boundary surfaces (here the number of unit bricks in the construction). But that conservation does not extend as yet to what has been termed 'occupied volume', i.e. the amount of space occupied by the object as a whole in relation to other objects round about. Thus a long row of 36 bricks put into a basinful of water is not thought to take up the same room as a different arrangement of the self-same bricks. And even when a block of bricks immersed in a basin of water is held to conserve its interior volume, this fact does not ensure conservation of the volume of water which is complementary.

Substage 3b usually begins around 8–9. Children now begin to measure correctly, using the unit-cubes as units, but they still do not carry out mathematical multiplication, which means they cannot establish numerical relations between lengths or areas and volumes as such. Their first attempts at calculating interior volume may be summed up as follows: Either they equate the volume with a given number of unit cubes, in which case the number is taken from one of the boundary surfaces, or else they equate it with the number of unit cubes which it takes to surround the model. Though measurements in terms of units of length are made in three dimensions, the children cannot understand how by multiplying these lengths they would arrive at products in terms of square or cubic units.

It is not until stage 4, i.e. at the level of formal operations, that children achieve the above understanding. And equally it is only at this stage that there is conservation of volume relative to the surrounding spatial medium, as against mere conservation of 'interior volume', that is, volume as defined by boundary surfaces.

PART FIVE

Conclusions

XV

The construction of Euclidean space: three levels

In the construction of Euclidean space, we may distinguish three levels of achievement. The first at substage 3a is represented by the qualitative operations in conservation of distance, length, area, and interior volume and the conservation of congruences in the process of transfer from one position to another.

The second level—at substage 3b—involves the achievement of simple operations, the measurement of length in one, two or three dimensions, the construction of metric co-ordinate systems and a first beginning of the measurement of angles and areas. The final level is reached at stage 4 when areas and volumes are calculated—only now do we find mathematical multiplication being used to co-ordinate the results of multiplicative logical operations and simple measurement, and only at this stage is there conservation of volume relative to the surrounding spatial medium.